90-Minute Shakespeare:

A MIDSUMMER NIGHT'S DREAM

By William Shakespeare
Adapted by Diane Timmerman

YOUNG ACTORS SERIES

A SMITH AND KRAUS BOOK

For Steve, Charis, and Barek

*And for my students and colleagues
at Butler University*

A Smith and Kraus Book
Published by Smith and Kraus, Inc.
177 Lyme Road, Hanover, NH 03755

First Edition: July 2001
10 9 8 7 6 5 4 3 2 1

*Cover and Text Design
by Julia Hill Gignoux, Freedom Hill Design
Cover Art: Photograhy by Brent Smith
Original Poster Design by Phil Eihacker
Blaine Hogan as Puck
Author Photo by Ed Moss*

The Library of Congress Cataloging-In-Publication Data
Timmerman, Diane.
90-Minute Shakespeare / by William Shakespeare ; adapted by Diane Timmerman.
—1st ed.
p. cm. — (Young actors series)
Contents: [v.1]. Romeo and Juliet — [v.2]. A midsummer night's dream
Summary: Presents scripts for two of William Shakespeare's classic plays,
edited so that they can be performed in ninety minutes.

ISBN 1-57525-238-4 Romeo and Juliet
ISBN 1-57525-290-2 A Midsummer Night's Dream

1. Shakespeare, William, 1564–1616—Adaptations—Juvenile literature.
[1. Shakespeare, William, 1564–1616—Plays.] I. Title: Ninety-minute Shakespeare.
II. Shakespeare, William 1564–1616. III. Title. IV. Young actors series.
PR2877 .T5 2001
822.3'3—dc21
2001034392

Introduction

Lovers chase each other through the enchanted landscape of their dreams. The world gets turned upside down as fairies play tricks, tradesmen rehearse plays, and the magic and mystery of love is revealed. Why would anyone want to shorten Shakespeare's most popular comedy? For me, the reasons for adapting and directing a ninety-minute *A Midsummer Night's Dream* are compelling. I love Shakespeare's images, characters, and stories. I marvel at the immediacy of the language 400 years after the words were penned. I despair when I sit through painstaking productions that alienate audiences because of their length. Strong evidence suggests that the original running times of Shakespeare's plays were much briefer than our current productions. By all accounts the Elizabethan productions zipped by at a lively, entertaining pace, their audience's ears hearing with the same dexterous speed as our modern-day eyes see. I wanted to capture that zestful spirit for contemporary audiences. And so, without altering Shakespeare's words, I edited this great play (and four others in this series) to its essential core. Shakespeare's characters still speak their lines in magnificent iambic pentameter and prose; they just speak fewer of them. Is this kosher? What would Bill think? Is it wrong to shorten these sacred, canonical plays? I actually think it is okay. And I think Bill would agree. Since talking and listening at the Elizabethan rate is not possible for us, surely he wouldn't mind if we occasionally shortened his scripts. Bill valued entertaining his audiences and just might approve of a running time that leaves audiences wanting to see another Shakespeare production—maybe even a full-length one. He'd undoubtedly prefer that reaction to exhausted audiences, exiting the theater vowing never to return again.

Who might use this *A Midsummer Night's Dream* script? Equity theaters operating under the ninety-minute Theater for Young Audiences contract, colleges, high schools, middle schools, and community theaters—any group desiring a shorter running time to satisfy their own needs or those of their audience. For me, this adaptation saw its first life as a production of the Butler Essential Shakespeare Series at Butler University in Indianapolis. Wanting to provide our Department of Theatre students with an annual opportunity to perform Shakespeare and desiring to create an educational outreach program to area middle and high school students, the Butler Essential Shakespeare Series was born. Each year, I adapted and directed one of the plays in this series. During the rehearsal period, cast and crew members would travel with me to area schools where we would do scenes from the play and Shakespearean acting workshops. The highlight of these visits was the informal conversation between the college students and the not-too-much-younger middle and high school students. How do you understand what the language means, the younger students wanted to know. With pride the college students would explain their process—how they studied the text, made the words their own, and ultimately reveled in the sheer thrill of playing Shakespeare. These conversations, along with the raucous laughter and rapt attention during the student matinees, proved what everyone in education knows: The message is most powerful when it comes not from on high, but from a near peer. Witnessing students only a few years older than them succeed in bold, visceral Shakespearean performances left indelible delight in our young audiences. The weeks of losing the battle to understand the bard (despite help from twenty-year-old videos) melted away when these students saw that Shakespeare was comprehensible, relevant, and fun! That the student matinees were successful was not a surprise—that the general public embraced the ninety-minute format was. Our evening performances became campus and citywide events. The shorter timeframe worked wonders for jaded adults who had sworn off Shakespeare. Elated at the end of the comedies, moved at the end of the tragedies, these grown-ups left the theater happy to have been there. The most uttered comment I heard was: "What was cut? That seemed like the whole play." Perhaps the pendulum will swing back in this sound-bite age of ours. We can always hope that channel surfing will be reduced and attention spans will lengthen. Until then, my text-lover status notwithstanding, I choose to bring people back to the theater to love Shakespeare—if only so they will once again find the courage to see a full-length production.

How did I edit this script? Let me count the ways. Mostly by trimming each existing scene. In a few cases, by eliminating small scenes and characters altogether. Functioning as part–director, part-iambic pentameter police, my editing goal was to create a playable script that respected the verse, the characters, and the story. Conceptual ideas of how I might direct *Midsummer* no doubt influenced the editing choices I made. (And editing the play gave me a headstart on the directing process.) Many cuts were easy to make; other choices were more painful. Although the adaptation was mainly completed before the rehearsal process began, invaluable tweaking took place as the actors played the text on their feet. Only then did some redundancies and leaps in logic emerge. Spirited debate over the intricacies of the text reigned during rehearsals, with actors comparing their shortened scenes to the full-length versions, filling up their performances with the power of the full text. For this play, I was able to retain all major characters and plotlines. I did cut the Philostrate and conflated Titania's four fairies into three. But the lovers still go through all of their mistaken identity foibles and the fairies do have their fun at the mortals' expense. Act Five's "Pyramus and Thisbe," played by the mechanicals, is much briefer than the original, but still works like gangbusters. For the occasional tricky editing maneuver, I confess to altering a word here or there to make the action coherent. Otherwise, the words are Shakespeare's.

How to produce this play? Many groups using this script already have a clear idea of their production goals. I offer a few tips here that might prove helpful for some. This adaptation is intentionally devoid of the translation notes found in most Shakespeare editions, enabling this book to function as a script. It is understood that the director, designers, and cast members will use full-length editions of *A Midsummer Night's Dream* for clarification of individual words as well as larger plot and action questions. If a transition appears awkward in the adaptation, revisit the full-length script, where you will usually find that the transition can be accomplished through physical action on the stage. Indeed, the success of a ninety-minute Shakespeare production lies in the physicality of the staging. Because much of the language has been cut, the story must be told in stage pictures and through physical movement—even more than one might employ in full-length productions. And because movement adds time, your first read-through may finish in only fifty minutes or less. During the course of the rehearsal period, when physical action, sound cues, music, dances, and fights are added, the running time will sneak back up to ninety minutes. All of these elements will enhance the production, adding structure and helping to tell the story. For *Midsummer*, sound and movement can be used effectively in many places. The meeting of Oberon and Titania in Act One and their reunification in Act Four is well served by music and dance, as is the return of everyone to Athens at the top of Act Five. Tremendous fun can be had with the fairies' physical movement and the lovers' slugfests. Whether you are utilizing a classical or contemporary sound, brief transitional music makes leaps in location and time clear.

The cast list for *Midsummer* is large; roles may be doubled depending on the needs of the organization. Many productions opt to double Theseus and Hippolyta with Oberon and Titania. (To remedy the opposite problem, some productions employ large fairy entourages for Titania and Oberon, servants for Theseus and Hippolyta, and extra, nonspeaking mechanicals.) Some roles may be played nontraditionally, a practice that works particularly well with Shakespeare. Casting women to play male roles (as men) works for the mechanicals. Some male characters may, with a change of pronouns, simply be switched to female characters: for *Midsummer*, Egeus easily becomes Hermia's mother. Traditionally, Titania's fairies are female and Oberon's are male, but reversing that might be fun. All of the fairies can also work well as androgynous beings. Color-blind casting works well for any role.

Everyone involved in theater knows it is a team sport. This script was successfully adapted and produced because I have been lucky enough to work with wonderful colleagues and amazing students whose talent and enthusiasm made the Butler Essential Shakespeare Series a joyful artistic enterprise. To the entire company of *A Midsummer Night's Dream*, I say "Thank you!"

Artistic projects are born out of an abundance of the soul, an overflowing of love and passion so great one must express it in a way that transcends the everyday language of our lives. Only by being blessed with the love of my best friend and husband, Steve Webb, and the inspiration of our children, Charis and Barek, do I find the courage to work on great Shakespearean texts. Their love and Shakespeare's words make me feel small and humbled—and completely invincible.

A *Midsummer Night's Dream* was first performed in the Lilly Hall Studio Theatre at Butler University in Indianapolis, Indiana, on October 18, 2000. It was subsequently presented in Clowes Memorial Hall on October 24, 2000. The cast was as follows:

THESEUS	Monte Tapplar
HIPPOLYTA	Margaret Len Stewart
EGEUS	Heather Clark
HERMIA	Kim Biss
LYSANDER	Tavi Stutz
DEMETRIUS	Zach McCoy
HELENA	Margaret Murray
QUINCE/Prologue	Neil Sqrow
BOTTOM/Pyramus	John Hammerle
FLUTE/Thisbe	Tony Majewski
STARVELING/Moonshine	Matthew Rozek
SNOUT/Wall	Neil Herndon
SNUG/Lion	Ronnie Gilliam
PUCK	Blaine Hogan
OBERON	Andrew Ahrens
TITANIA	Steph Johnson
PEASEBLOSSOM	Mychela Burke
COBWEB	Mandy Keller
MUSTARDSEED	Andrea Kehler
Director	Diane Timmerman
Scenic/Lighting Designer	Madeleine Sobota
Costume Designer	Nicole Sobota
Sound Designer	Frank Felice
Choreographer	Cynthia Pratt
Makeup Designer	Kim Osborne
Technical Director	Glen Thoreson
Props Master	Susan Benson
Stage Manager	Liz Freeman

CAST OF CHARACTERS

Theseus, Duke of Athens

Hippolyta, Queen of the Amazons, betrothed to Theseus

Egeus, Father of Hermia

Lysander, in love with Hermia

Demetrius, preferred by Egeus as a match for Hermia

Hermia, in love with Lysander

Helena, in love with Demetrius

Oberon, King of the Fairies

Titania, Queen of the Fairies

Puck or Robin Goodfellow, Oberon's jester and attendant

Peaseblossom, Fairy attending on Titania

Cobweb, Fairy attending on Titania

Mustardseed, Fairy attending on Titania

Peter Quince, carpenter (Prologue in 'Pyramus and Thisbe')

Nick Bottom, weaver (Pyramus)

Francis Flute, bellows-mender (Thisbe)

Tom Snout, tinker (Wall)

Robin Starveling, tailor (Moonshine)

Snug, joiner (Lion)

Act 1, Scene 1

Athens. The palace of THESEUS.

(Enter THESEUS and HIPPOLYTA.)

THESEUS
    Now, fair Hippolyta, our nuptial hour
    Draws on apace; four happy days bring in
    Another moon: but, O, methinks, how slow
    This old moon wanes!

HIPPOLYTA
    Four days will quickly steep themselves in night;
    Four nights will quickly dream away the time;
    And then the moon, like to a silver bow
    New-bent in heaven, shall behold the night
    Of our solemnities.

THESEUS
    Hippolyta, I woo'd thee with my sword,
    And won thy love, doing thee injuries;
    But I will wed thee in another key,
    With pomp, with triumph and with revelling.

(Enter EGEUS, HERMIA, LYSANDER, and DEMETRIUS.)

EGEUS
    Happy be Theseus, our renowned duke!

THESEUS
    Thanks, good Egeus: what's the news with thee?

EGEUS
    Full of vexation come I, with complaint
    Against my child, my daughter Hermia.

Stand forth, Demetrius. My noble lord,
This man hath my consent to marry her.
Stand forth, Lysander: and my gracious duke,
This man hath bewitch'd the bosom of my child;
Thou, thou, Lysander, thou hast given her rhymes,
And interchanged love-tokens with my child:
Thou hast by moonlight at her window sung,
With feigning voice verses of feigning love,
With cunning hast thou filch'd my daughter's heart,
Turn'd her obedience, which is due to me,
To stubborn harshness: and, my gracious duke,
Be it so she will not here before your grace
Consent to marry with Demetrius,
I beg the ancient privilege of Athens,
As she is mine, I may dispose of her:
Which shall be either to this gentleman
Or to her death, according to our law
Immediately provided in that case.

THESEUS
What say you, Hermia?
Demetrius is a worthy gentleman.

HERMIA
I would my father look'd but with my eyes.

THESEUS
Rather your eyes must with his judgment look.

HERMIA
I know not by what power I am made bold,
But I beseech your grace that I may know
The worst that may befall me in this case,
If I refuse to wed Demetrius.

THESEUS
    Either to die the death or to abjure
    For ever the society of men.
    Therefore, fair Hermia, question your desires;
    Whether, if you yield not to your father's choice,
    You can endure the livery of a nun.
    Take time to pause; and, by the next new moon—
    The sealing-day betwixt my love and me—
    Upon that day either prepare to die
    For disobedience to your father's will,
    Or else to wed Demetrius, as he would;
    Or on Diana's altar to protest
    For aye austerity and single life.

DEMETRIUS
    Relent, sweet Hermia: and, Lysander, yield
    Thy crazed title to my certain right.

LYSANDER
    You have her father's love, Demetrius;
    Let me have Hermia's: do you marry him.

EGEUS
    Scornful Lysander! True, he hath my love,
    And what is mine my love shall render him.
    And she is mine, and all my right of her
    I do estate unto Demetrius.

LYSANDER
    I am, my lord, as well derived as he,
    As well possess'd; my love is more than his;
    And, which is more than all these boasts can be,
    I am beloved of beauteous Hermia:
    Why should not I then prosecute my right?
    Demetrius, I'll avouch it to his head,
    Made love to Nedar's daughter, Helena,

And won her soul; and she, sweet lady, dotes,
Devoutly dotes, dotes in idolatry,
Upon this spotted and inconstant man.

THESEUS
I must confess that I have heard so much,
And with Demetrius thought to have spoke thereof;
But, being over-full of self-affairs,
My mind did lose it. But, Demetrius, come;
And come, Egeus; you shall go with me;
For you, fair Hermia, look you arm yourself
To fit your fancies to your father's will;
Or else the law of Athens yields you up
To death, or to a vow of single life.
Come, my Hippolyta: what cheer, my love?

(Exeunt all but LYSANDER and HERMIA.)

LYSANDER
How now, my love! Why is your cheek so pale?
How chance the roses there do fade so fast?

HERMIA
Belike for want of rain, which I could well
Beteem them from the tempest of my eyes.

LYSANDER
Ay me! For aught that I could ever read,
Could ever hear by tale or history,
The course of true love never did run smooth;
But, either it was different in blood—

HERMIA
O cross! Too high to be enthrall'd to low.

LYSANDER
Or else misgraffed in respect of years—

HERMIA
O spite! Too old to be engaged to young.

LYSANDER
Or else it stood upon the choice of friends—

HERMIA
O hell! To choose love by another's eyes.
If then true lovers have been ever cross'd,
It stands as an edict in destiny:
Then let us teach our trial patience.

LYSANDER
A good persuasion: therefore, hear me, Hermia.
I have a widow aunt, a dowager,
From Athens is her house remote seven leagues;
There, gentle Hermia, may I marry thee;
And to that place the sharp Athenian law
Cannot pursue us. If thou lov'st me then,
Steal forth thy father's house tomorrow night;
And in the wood, a league without the town,
There will I stay for thee.

HERMIA
My good Lysander!
I swear to thee, by Cupid's strongest bow,
In that same place thou hast appointed me,
Tomorrow truly will I meet with thee.

LYSANDER
Keep promise, love. Look, here comes Helena.

(*Enter HELENA.*)

HERMIA

God speed fair Helena! Whither away?

HELENA

Call you me fair? That fair again unsay.
Demetrius loves your fair: O happy fair!
Your eyes are lode-stars; and your tongue's sweet air
More tuneable than lark to shepherd's ear.
O, teach me how you look, and with what art
You sway the motion of Demetrius' heart.

HERMIA

I frown upon him, yet he loves me still.

HELENA

O that your frowns would teach my smiles such skill!

HERMIA

I give him curses, yet he gives me love.

HELENA

O that my prayers could such affection move!

HERMIA

The more I hate, the more he follows me.

HELENA

The more I love, the more he hateth me.

HERMIA

His folly, Helena, is no fault of mine.

HELENA

None, but your beauty: would that fault were mine!

HERMIA
Take comfort: he no more shall see my face;
Lysander and myself will fly this place.

LYSANDER
Helen, to you our minds we will unfold:
Tomorrow night, when Phoebe doth behold
Her silver visage in the watery glass,
Decking with liquid pearl the bladed grass,
A time that lovers' flights doth still conceal,
Through Athens' gates have we devised to steal.

HERMIA
And in the wood, where often you and I
Upon faint primrose-beds were wont to lie,
Emptying our bosoms of their counsel sweet,
There my Lysander and myself shall meet;
And thence from Athens turn away our eyes,
To seek new friends and stranger companies.
Farewell, sweet playfellow: pray thou for us;
And good luck grant thee thy Demetrius!
Keep word, Lysander: we must starve our sight
From lovers' food till morrow deep midnight.

LYSANDER
I will, my Hermia.

(Exit HERMIA.)

Helena, adieu:
As you on him, Demetrius dote on you!

(Exit.)

HELENA
How happy some o'er other some can be!

Through Athens I am thought as fair as she.
But what of that? Demetrius thinks not so;
He will not know what all but he do know.
And as he errs, doting on Hermia's eyes,
So I, admiring of his qualities.
I will go tell him of fair Hermia's flight:
Then to the wood will he tomorrow night
Pursue her; and for this intelligence
If I have thanks, it is a dear expense:
But herein mean I to enrich my pain,
To have his sight thither and back again.

(Exit.)

Act 1, Scene 2

Athens. QUINCE'S house.

(Enter QUINCE, SNUG, BOTTOM, FLUTE, SNOUT, and STARVELING.)

QUINCE
Is all our company here?

BOTTOM
You were best to call them generally, man by man, according to the scrip.

QUINCE
Here is the scroll of every man's name, which is thought fit, through all Athens, to play in our interlude before the duke and the duchess, on his wedding-day at night.

BOTTOM
First, good Peter Quince, say what the play treats on, then read the names of the actors, and so grow to a point.

QUINCE
Marry, our play is, *The most lamentable comedy, and most cruel death of Pyramus and Thisby.*

BOTTOM
A very good piece of work, I assure you, and a merry. Now, good Peter Quince, call forth your actors by the scroll. Masters, spread yourselves.

QUINCE
Answer as I call you. Nick Bottom, the weaver.

BOTTOM
Ready. Name what part I am for, and proceed.

QUINCE
You, Nick Bottom, are set down for Pyramus.

BOTTOM
What is Pyramus? A lover, or a tyrant?

QUINCE
A lover, that kills himself most gallant for love.

BOTTOM
That will ask some tears in the true performing of
it: if I do it, let the audience look to their
eyes; I will move storms, I will condole in some
measure. Name the rest of the players.

QUINCE
Francis Flute, the bellows-mender.

FLUTE
Here, Peter Quince.

QUINCE
Flute, you must take Thisby on you.

FLUTE
What is Thisby? A wandering knight?

QUINCE
It is the lady that Pyramus must love.

FLUTE
Nay, faith, let me not play a woman; I have a beard coming.

QUINCE
That's all one: you shall play it in a mask, and
you may speak as small as you will.

BOTTOM
And I may hide my face, let me play Thisby too, I'll
speak in a monstrous little voice. 'Thisne,
Thisne;' 'Ah, Pyramus, lover dear! thy Thisby dear,
and lady dear!'

QUINCE
No, no; you must play Pyramus: and, Flute, you Thisby.

BOTTOM
Well, proceed.

QUINCE
Robin Starveling, the tailor.

STARVELING
Here, Peter Quince.

QUINCE
Robin Starveling, you must play Thisby's mother.
Tom Snout, the tinker.

SNOUT
Here, Peter Quince.

QUINCE
You, Pyramus' father: myself, Thisby's father:
Snug, the joiner; you, the lion's part: and, I
hope, here is a play fitted.

SNUG

Have you the lion's part written? Pray you, if it
be, give it me, for I am slow of study.

QUINCE

You may do it extempore, for it is nothing but roaring.

BOTTOM

Let me play the lion too: I will roar,
that I will make the duke say 'Let him roar again,
let him roar again.'

QUINCE

And you should do it too terribly, you would fright
the duchess and the ladies, that they would shriek;
and that were enough to hang us all.

ALL

That would hang us, every mother's son.

BOTTOM

I will aggravate my voice so that I will roar you as
gently as any sucking dove; I will roar you and 'twere
any nightingale.

QUINCE

You can play no part but Pyramus; for Pyramus is a
sweet-faced man; a proper man, as one shall see in a
summer's day; a most lovely gentleman-like man:
therefore you must needs play Pyramus.

BOTTOM

Well, I will undertake it.

QUINCE

Masters, here are your parts: and I am to entreat you,

request you and desire you, to con them by tomorrow
night; and meet me in the palace wood, a mile without the
town, by moonlight; there will we rehearse.

BOTTOM
We will meet; and there we may rehearse most
obscenely and courageously. Take pains; be perfect: adieu.

QUINCE
At the duke's oak we meet.

BOTTOM
Enough; hold or cut bow-strings.

(Exeunt.)

Act 2, Scene 1

A wood near Athens.

(Enter, from opposite sides, PEASEBLOSSOM and PUCK.)

PUCK
> How now, spirit, whither wander you?

PEASEBLOSSOM
> I do wander everywhere
> Swifter than the moon's sphere;
> And I serve the fairy queen,
> To dew her orbs upon the green.
> I must go seek some dewdrops here
> And hang a pearl in every cowslip's ear.
> Farewell, thou lob of spirits; I'll be gone:
> Our queen and all our elves come here anon.

PUCK
> The king doth keep his revels here tonight:
> Take heed the queen come not within his sight;
> For Oberon is passing fell and wrath,
> Because that she as her attendant hath
> A lovely boy, stolen from an Indian king;
> She never had so sweet a changeling;
> And jealous Oberon would have the child
> Knight of his train, to trace the forests wild;
> But she perforce withholds the loved boy,
> Crowns him with flowers and makes him all her joy.

PEASEBLOSSOM
> Either I mistake your shape and making quite,
> Or else you are that shrewd and knavish sprite
> Call'd Robin Goodfellow: are not you he
> That frights the maidens of the villagery?
> Those that Hobgoblin call you and sweet Puck,

You do their work, and they shall have good luck:
Are not you he?

PUCK
Thou speak'st aright;
I am that merry wanderer of the night.
But, room, fairy! Here comes Oberon.

PEASEBLOSSOM
And here my mistress. Would that he were gone!

(Enter, from one side, OBERON, with his train; from the other, TITANIA, with her train.)

OBERON
Ill met by moonlight, proud Titania.

TITANIA
What, jealous Oberon! Fairies, skip hence:
I have forsworn his bed and company.

OBERON
Tarry, rash wanton: am not I thy lord?

TITANIA
Then I must be thy lady. But why art thou here,
Come from the farthest step of India?
But that, forsooth, the bouncing Amazon,
Your buskin'd mistress and your warrior love,
To Theseus must be wedded, and you come
To give their bed joy and prosperity.

OBERON
How canst thou thus for shame, Titania,
Glance at my credit with Hippolyta,
Knowing I know thy love to Theseus?

TITANIA

These are the forgeries of jealousy:
And never, since the middle summer's spring,
Met we on hill, in dale, forest or mead,
To dance our ringlets to the whistling wind,
But with thy brawls thou hast disturb'd our sport.
Therefore the winds, piping to us in vain,
As in revenge, have suck'd up from the sea
Contagious fogs; which falling in the land
Have every pelting river made so proud
That they have overborne their continents:
Therefore the moon, the governess of floods,
Pale in her anger, washes all the air,
That rheumatic diseases do abound:
And thorough this distemperature we see
The seasons alter: the spring, the summer,
The childing autumn, angry winter, change
Their wonted liveries, and the mazed world,
By their increase, now knows not which is which.
And this same progeny of evils comes
From our debate, from our dissension.

OBERON

Do you amend it then; it lies in you.
Why should Titania cross her Oberon?
I do but beg a little changeling boy,
To be my henchman.

TITANIA

Set your heart at rest:
The fairy land buys not the child of me.
His mother was a votress of my order:
And, in the spiced Indian air, by night,
Full often hath she gossip'd by my side.
But she, being mortal, of that boy did die;
And for her sake do I rear up her boy,
And for her sake I will not part with him.

OBERON
How long within this wood intend you stay?

TITANIA
Perchance till after Theseus' wedding-day.
If you will patiently dance in our round
And see our moonlight revels, go with us.

OBERON
Give me that boy, and I will go with thee.

TITANIA
Not for thy fairy kingdom. Fairies, away!
We shall chide downright, if I longer stay.

(Exit TITANIA with her train.)

OBERON
Well, go thy way: thou shalt not from this grove
Till I torment thee for this injury.
My gentle Puck, come hither.
Fetch me that flower; the herb I show'd thee once:
The juice of it on sleeping eyelids laid
Will make or man or woman madly dote
Upon the next live creature that it sees.
Fetch me this herb; and be thou here again
Ere the leviathan can swim a league.

PUCK
I'll put a girdle round about the earth
In forty minutes.

(Exit.)

OBERON
Having once this juice,

I'll watch Titania when she is asleep,
And drop the liquor of it in her eyes.
The next thing then she waking looks upon,
Be it on lion, bear, or wolf, or bull,
She shall pursue it with the soul of love:
And ere I take this charm from off her sight,
As I can take it with another herb,
I'll make her render up her page to me.
But who comes here? I am invisible;
And I will overhear their conference.

(Enter DEMETRIUS and HELENA following him.)

DEMETRIUS

I love thee not, therefore pursue me not.
Where is Lysander and fair Hermia?
The one I'll slay, the other slayeth me.
Thou told'st me they were stolen unto this wood;
Hence, get thee gone, and follow me no more.

HELENA

You draw me, you hard-hearted adamant!

DEMETRIUS

Do I entice you? Do I speak you fair?
Or, rather, do I not in plainest truth
Tell you, I do not, nor I cannot love you?

HELENA

And even for that do I love you the more.
I am your spaniel; and, Demetrius,
The more you beat me, I will fawn on you:
Use me but as your spaniel, spurn me, strike me,
Neglect me, lose me; only give me leave,
Unworthy as I am, to follow you.
What worser place can I beg in your love—

And yet a place of high respect with me—
Than to be used as you use your dog?

DEMETRIUS
Tempt not too much the hatred of my spirit;
For I am sick when I do look on thee.

HELENA
And I am sick when I look not on you.

DEMETRIUS
I'll run from thee and hide me in the brakes,
And leave thee to the mercy of wild beasts.

HELENA
The wildest hath not such a heart as you.

DEMETRIUS
Let me go:
Or, if thou follow me, do not believe
But I shall do thee mischief in the wood.

HELENA
Ay, in the temple, in the town, the field,
You do me mischief. Fie, Demetrius!
Your wrongs do set a scandal on my sex.
We cannot fight for love, as men may do;
We should be wooed and were not made to woo.

(Exit DEMETRIUS.)

I'll follow thee and make a heaven of hell,
To die upon the hand I love so well.

(Exit.)

OBERON
    Fare thee well, nymph: ere he do leave this grove,
    Thou shalt fly him and he shall seek thy love.

(Re-enter PUCK.)

    Hast thou the flower there? Welcome, wanderer.

PUCK
    Ay, there it is.

OBERON
    I pray thee, give it me.
    I know a bank where the wild thyme blows,
    Where oxlips and the nodding violet grows,
    There sleeps Titania sometime of the night,
    Lull'd in these flowers with dances and delight;
    And with the juice of this I'll streak her eyes,
    And make her full of hateful fantasies.
    Take thou some of it, and seek through this grove:
    A sweet Athenian lady is in love
    With a disdainful youth; anoint his eyes,
    But do it when the next thing he espies
    May be the lady. Thou shalt know the man
    By the Athenian garments he hath on.
    Effect it with some care, that he may prove
    More fond on her than she upon her love:
    And look thou meet me ere the first cock crow.

PUCK
    Fear not, my lord! Your servant shall do so.

    (Exeunt.)

Act 2, Scene 2

Another part of the wood.

(Enter TITANIA, with her train.)

TITANIA
  Come, now a fairy song; sing me now asleep.

(The Fairies sing.)

COBWEB
  Hence, away! Now all is well.

(Exeunt Fairies. TITANIA sleeps.)
(Enter OBERON and squeezes the flower on TITANIA's eyelids.)

OBERON
  What thou seest when thou dost wake,
  Do it for thy true-love take,
  Love and languish for his sake:
  Be it ounce, or cat, or bear,
  When thou wak'st, it is thy dear:
  Wake when some vile thing is near.

(Exit.)

(Enter LYSANDER and HERMIA.)

LYSANDER
  Fair love, you faint with wandering in the wood;
  And to speak troth, I have forgot our way:
  We'll rest us, Hermia, if you think it good,
  And tarry for the comfort of the day.

HERMIA

Be it so, Lysander: find you out a bed;
For I upon this bank will rest my head.

LYSANDER

One turf shall serve as pillow for us both;
One heart, one bed, two bosoms and one troth.

HERMIA

Nay, good Lysander; for my sake, my dear,
Lie further off yet, do not lie so near.

LYSANDER

O, take the sense, sweet, of my innocence!
Love takes the meaning in love's conference;
I mean, that my heart unto yours is knit
So that but one heart we can make of it:
Two bosoms interchained with an oath,
So then two bosoms and a single troth.
Then by your side no bed-room me deny;
For lying so, Hermia, I do not lie.

HERMIA

Lysander riddles very prettily:
Now much beshrew my manners and my pride,
If Hermia meant to say Lysander lied.
But, gentle friend, for love and courtesy
Lie further off, in human modesty;
Such separation as may well be said
Becomes a virtuous bachelor and a maid.

LYSANDER

Here is my bed: sleep give thee all his rest!

HERMIA

With half that wish the wisher's eyes be press'd!

(They sleep.)
(Enter PUCK.)

PUCK
    Through the forest have I gone,
    But Athenian found I none—Who is here?
    Weeds of Athens he doth wear:
    This is he, my master said,
    Despised the Athenian maid;
    And here the maiden, sleeping sound,
    On the dank and dirty ground.
    Churl, upon thy eyes I throw
    All the power this charm doth owe.
    When thou wak'st, let love forbid
    Sleep his seat on thy eyelid:
    So awake when I am gone;
    For I must now to Oberon.

(Exit.)
(Enter DEMETRIUS and HELENA, running.)

HELENA
    Stay, though thou kill me, sweet Demetrius.

DEMETRIUS
    I charge thee, hence, and do not haunt me thus.

HELENA
    O, wilt thou darkling leave me? Do not so!

DEMETRIUS
    Stay, on thy peril: I alone will go.

(Exit.)

HELENA

O, I am out of breath in this fond chase!
The more my prayer, the lesser is my grace.
Happy is Hermia, wheresoe'er she lies;
For she hath blessed and attractive eyes.
How came her eyes so bright? Not with salt tears:
If so, my eyes are oftener wash'd than hers.
No, no, I am as ugly as a bear;
For beasts that meet me run away for fear.
But who is here? Lysander! On the ground!
Dead, or asleep? I see no blood, no wound.
Lysander if you live, good sir, awake!

LYSANDER

(Awaking.) And run through fire I will for thy sweet sake!
Transparent Helena! Nature shows art,
That through thy bosom makes me see thy heart.
Where is Demetrius? O, how fit a word
Is that vile name to perish on my sword!

HELENA

Do not say so, Lysander; say not so.
What though he love your Hermia? Lord, what though?
Yet Hermia still loves you: then be content.

LYSANDER

Content with Hermia! No; I do repent
The tedious minutes I with her have spent.
Not Hermia but Helena I love:
Who will not change a raven for a dove?
The will of man is by his reason sway'd;
And reason says you are the worthier maid.

HELENA

Wherefore was I to this keen mockery born?
When at your hands did I deserve this scorn?

Is't not enough, is't not enough, young man,
That I did never, no, nor never can,
Deserve a sweet look from Demetrius' eye,
But you must flout my insufficiency?
Good troth, you do me wrong, good sooth, you do,
In such disdainful manner me to woo.
But fare you well: perforce I must confess
I thought you lord of more true gentleness.

(Exit.)

LYSANDER
She sees not Hermia. Hermia, sleep thou there:
And never mayst thou come Lysander near!
For as a surfeit of the sweetest things
The deepest loathing to the stomach brings,
So thou, my surfeit and my heresy,
Of all be hated, but the most of me!
And, all my powers, address your love and might
To honour Helen and to be her knight!

(Exit.)

HERMIA
(Awaking.) Ay me, for pity! What a dream was here!
Lysander, look how I do quake with fear—
Methought a serpent ate my heart away,
And you sat smiling at his cruel prey.
Lysander! What, removed? Lysander! Lord!
What, out of hearing? Gone? No sound, no word?
Alack, where are you? Speak and if you hear;
Speak, of all loves! I swoon almost with fear.
No? Then I well perceive you are not nigh
Either death or you I'll find immediately.

(Exit.)

Act 3, Scene 1

The wood. TITANIA lying asleep.

(Enter QUINCE, SNUG, BOTTOM, FLUTE, SNOUT, and STARVELING.)

BOTTOM
> Are we all met?

QUINCE
> Pat, pat; and here's a marvellous convenient place
> for our rehearsal.

BOTTOM
> Peter Quince!

QUINCE
> What sayest thou, bully Bottom?

BOTTOM
> There are things in this comedy of Pyramus and
> Thisby that will never please. First, Pyramus must
> draw a sword to kill himself; which the ladies
> cannot abide. How answer you that?

SNOUT
> By'r lakin, a parlous fear.

STARVELING
> I believe we must leave the killing out, when all is done.

BOTTOM
> Not a whit: I have a device to make all well.
> Write me a prologue; and let the prologue seem to

say, we will do no harm with our swords, and that
Pyramus is not killed indeed; and, for the more
better assurance, tell them that I, Pyramus, am not
Pyramus, but Bottom the weaver: this will put them
out of fear.

SNOUT
Will not the ladies be afeard of the lion?

STARVELING
I fear it, I promise you.

BOTTOM
A lion among ladies is a most dreadful thing. Nay,
he himself must speak through, saying 'Fair ladies,
I would entreat you, not to fear, not to tremble.
If you think I come hither as a lion, it were pity
of my life: no I am no such thing; I am a man as
other men are'—and there indeed let him name his
name, and tell them plainly he is Snug the joiner.

QUINCE
Well it shall be so. But there is two hard things:
that is, to bring the moonlight into a chamber; for
you know, Pyramus and Thisby meet by moonlight.

SNOUT
Doth the moon shine that night we play our play?

BOTTOM
A calendar, a calendar! Look in the almanac—find
out moonshine, find out moonshine!

QUINCE
Yes, it doth shine that night.

BOTTOM
> Why, then may you leave a casement of the great
> chamber window, where we play, open, and the moon
> may shine in at the casement.

QUINCE
> Then, there is another thing: we must have a wall in
> the great chamber; for Pyramus and Thisby, says the
> story, did talk through the chink of a wall.

SNOUT
> You can never bring in a wall. What say you, Bottom?

BOTTOM
> Some man or other must present Wall and let him
> hold his fingers thus, and through that cranny
> shall Pyramus and Thisby whisper.

QUINCE
> If that may be, then all is well. Come, sit down,
> every mother's son, and rehearse your parts.

(Enter PUCK behind.)

PUCK
> What hempen home-spuns have we swaggering here,
> So near the cradle of the fairy queen?
> What, a play toward? I'll be an auditor;
> An actor too, perhaps, if I see cause.

QUINCE
> Speak, Pyramus. Thisby, stand forth.

BOTTOM
> Thisby, the flowers of odious savours sweet—

QUINCE
　　Odorous! Odorous!

BOTTOM
　　—odours savours sweet:
　　So hath thy breath, my dearest Thisby dear.
　　But hark, a voice! Stay thou but here awhile,
　　And by and by I will to thee appear.

(Exit.)

PUCK
　　A stranger Pyramus than e'er played here.

(Exit.)

FLUTE
　　Must I speak now?

QUINCE
　　Ay, marry, must you; for you must understand he goes
　　but to see a noise that he heard, and is to come again.

FLUTE
　　Most radiant Pyramus, most lily-white of hue,
　　I'll meet thee, Pyramus, at Ninny's tomb.

QUINCE
　　'Ninus' tomb,' man! Why, you must not speak that
　　yet; that you answer to Pyramus. You speak all your
　　part at once, cues and all. Pyramus enter: your cue
　　is past; it is, 'never tire.'

FLUTE
　　O—As true as truest horse, that yet would
　　never tire.

(Re-enter PUCK, and BOTTOM with an ass's head.)

BOTTOM
  If I were fair, Thisby, I were only thine.

QUINCE
  O monstrous! O strange! We are haunted. Pray,
  masters, fly, masters! Help!

*(Exeunt QUINCE, SNUG, FLUTE, SNOUT, and
STARVELING.)*

BOTTOM
  Why do they run away? This is a knavery of them to
  make me afeard.

(Re-enter SNOUT.)

SNOUT
  O Bottom, thou art changed! What do I see on thee?

BOTTOM
  What do you see? You see an asshead of your own, do
  you?

(Exit SNOUT.)
(Re-enter QUINCE.)

QUINCE
  Bless thee, Bottom, bless thee! Thou art translated.

(Exit.)

BOTTOM
  I see their knavery. This is to make an ass of me;
  to fright me, if they could. But I will not stir

from this place, do what they can: I will walk up
and down here, and I will sing, that they shall hear
I am not afraid.

(Sings.)

TITANIA

(Awaking.) What angel wakes me from my flowery bed?
I pray thee, gentle mortal, sing again:
Mine ear is much enamour'd of thy note;
So is mine eye enthralled to thy shape;
And thy fair virtue's force perforce doth move me
On the first view to say, to swear, I love thee.

BOTTOM

Methinks, mistress, you should have little reason
for that: and yet, to say the truth, reason and
love keep little company together nowadays.

TITANIA

Thou art as wise as thou art beautiful.

BOTTOM

Not so, neither: but if I had wit enough to get out
of this wood, I have enough to serve mine own turn.

TITANIA

Out of this wood do not desire to go:
Thou shalt remain here, whether thou wilt or no.
I am a spirit of no common rate;
The summer still doth tend upon my state;
And I do love thee: therefore, go with me;
I'll give thee fairies to attend on thee,
And I will purge thy mortal grossness so
That thou shalt like an airy spirit go.
Peaseblossom! Cobweb! And my Mustardseed!

(Enter PEASEBLOSSOM, COBWEB, and MUSTARDSEED.)

PEASEBLOSSOM
  Ready.

COBWEB
  And I.

MUSTARDSEED
  And I.

ALL
  Where shall we go?

TITANIA
  Be kind and courteous to this gentleman;
  Feed him with apricots and dewberries,
  With purple grapes, green figs, and mulberries;
  And pluck the wings from painted butterflies
  To fan the moonbeams from his sleeping eyes.
  Nod to him, elves, and do him courtesies.

PEASEBLOSSOM
  Hail, mortal!

COBWEB
  Hail!

MUSTARDSEED
  Hail!

BOTTOM
  I cry your worship's mercy, heartily. I beseech your
  worship's name.

COBWEB

Cobweb.

BOTTOM

I shall desire you of more acquaintance, good Master
Cobweb. Your name, honest gentleman?

PEASEBLOSSOM

Peaseblossom.

BOTTOM

I pray you, commend me to Mistress Squash, your
mother. Your name, I beseech you, sir?

MUSTARDSEED

Mustardseed.

BOTTOM

I desire your more acquaintance, good Master
Mustardseed.

TITANIA

Come, wait upon him; lead him to my bower.
The moon methinks looks with a watery eye;
And when she weeps, weeps every little flower,
Lamenting some enforced chastity.
Tie up my love's tongue; bring him silently.

(Exeunt.)

Act 3, Scene 2

Another part of the wood.

(Enter OBERON.)

OBERON
    I wonder if Titania be awaked;
    Then what it was that next came in her eye,
    Which she must dote on in extremity.

(Enter PUCK.)

    Here comes my messenger. How now, mad spirit!
    What night-rule now about this haunted grove?

PUCK
    My mistress with a monster is in love.
    Near to her close and consecrated bower,
    While she was in her dull and sleeping hour,
    A crew of patches, rude mechanicals,
    That work for bread upon Athenian stalls,
    Were met together to rehearse a play
    Intended for great Theseus' nuptial-day.
    The shallowest thick-skin of that barren sort,
    Who Pyramus presented, in their sport
    Forsook his scene and enter'd in a brake
    When I did him at this advantage take,
    An ass's nole I fixed on his head.
    In a few moments, so it came to pass,
    Titania waked and straightway loved an ass.

OBERON
    This falls out better than I could devise.
    But hast thou yet latch'd the Athenian's eyes
    With the love-juice, as I did bid thee do?

PUCK
    I took him sleeping—that is finish'd too—
    And the Athenian woman by his side,
    That when he waked, of force she must be eyed.

(Enter HERMIA and DEMETRIUS.)

OBERON
    Stand close: this is the same Athenian.

PUCK
    This is the woman, but not this the man.

DEMETRIUS
    O, why rebuke you him that loves you so?
    Lay breath so bitter on your bitter foe.

HERMIA
    Now I but chide; but I should use thee worse,
    For thou, I fear, hast given me cause to curse.
    If thou hast slain Lysander in his sleep,
    Being o'er shoes in blood, plunge in the deep,
    And kill me too.
    It cannot be but thou hast murder'd him;
    So should a murderer look—so dead, so grim.

DEMETRIUS
    So should the murder'd look, and so should I,
    Pierced through the heart with your stern cruelty.

HERMIA
    What's this to my Lysander? Where is he?
    Ah, good Demetrius, wilt thou give him me?

DEMETRIUS
    I had rather give his carcass to my hounds.

HERMIA

    Out, dog! Out, cur! Thou driv'st me past the bounds
    Of maiden's patience. Hast thou slain him, then?
    Henceforth be never number'd among men!

DEMETRIUS

    You spend your passion on a misprised mood:
    I am not guilty of Lysander's blood;
    Nor is he dead, for aught that I can tell.

HERMIA

    I pray thee, tell me then that he is well.

DEMETRIUS

    And if I could, what should I get therefore?

HERMIA

    A privilege never to see me more.
    And from thy hated presence part I so:
    See me no more, whether he be dead or no.

(Exit.)

DEMETRIUS

    There is no following her in this fierce vein:
    Here therefore for a while I will remain.
    So sorrow's heaviness doth heavier grow
    For debt that bankrupt sleep doth sorrow owe:
    Which now in some slight measure it will pay,
    If for his tender here I make some stay.

(Lies down and sleeps.)

OBERON

    What hast thou done? Thou hast mistaken quite
    And laid the love-juice on some true love's sight.

About the wood go swifter than the wind,
And Helena of Athens look thou find.
All fancy-sick she is and pale of cheer
With sighs of love, that costs the fresh blood dear.
By some illusion see thou bring her here:
I'll charm his eyes against she do appear.

PUCK
    I go, I go; look how I go,
    Swifter than arrow from the Tartar's bow.

(Exit.)

OBERON
    Flower of this purple dye,
    Hit with Cupid's archery,
    Sink in apple of his eye.
    When his love he doth espy,
    Let her shine as gloriously
    As the Venus of the sky.
    When thou wak'st, if she be by,
    Beg of her for remedy.

(Re-enter PUCK.)

PUCK
    Captain of our fairy band,
    Helena is here at hand;
    And the youth, mistook by me,
    Pleading for a lover's fee.
    Shall we their fond pageant see?
    Lord, what fools these mortals be!

OBERON
    Stand aside: the noise they make
    Will cause Demetrius to awake.

(Enter LYSANDER and HELENA.)

LYSANDER
> Why should you think that I should woo in scorn?

HELENA
> You do advance your cunning more and more.
> When truth kills truth, O devilish-holy fray!
> These vows are Hermia's: will you give her o'er?
> Weigh oath with oath, and you will nothing weigh.

LYSANDER
> I had no judgment when to her I swore.

HELENA
> Nor none, in my mind, now you give her o'er.

LYSANDER
> Demetrius loves her, and he loves not you.

DEMETRIUS
> *(Awaking.)* O Helena, goddess, nymph, perfect, divine!
> To what, my love, shall I compare thine eyne?
> Crystal is muddy. O, how ripe in show
> Thy lips, those kissing cherries, tempting grow!
> When thou hold'st up thy hand: O, let me kiss
> This princess of pure white, this seal of bliss!

HELENA
> O spite! O hell! I see you all are bent
> To set against me for your merriment.
> If you were civil and knew courtesy,
> You would not do me thus much injury.
> Can you not hate me, as I know you do,
> But you must join in souls to mock me too?

If you were men, as men you are in show,
You would not use a gentle lady so.
You both are rivals, and love Hermia;
And now both rivals, to mock Helena.

LYSANDER
You are unkind, Demetrius; be not so;
For you love Hermia—this you know I know—
And here, with all good will, with all my heart,
In Hermia's love I yield you up my part;
And yours of Helena to me bequeath,
Whom I do love and will do till my death.

HELENA
Never did mockers waste more idle breath.

DEMETRIUS
Lysander, keep thy Hermia; I will none:
If e'er I loved her, all that love is gone.
My heart to her but as guest-wise sojourn'd,
And now to Helen is it home return'd,
There to remain.

LYSANDER
Helen, it is not so.

DEMETRIUS
Look, where thy love comes; yonder is thy dear.

(Re-enter HERMIA.)

HERMIA
Thou art not by mine eye, Lysander, found;
Mine ear, I thank it, brought me to thy sound.
But why unkindly didst thou leave me so?

LYSANDER

    Why should he stay, whom love doth press to go?

HERMIA

    What love could press Lysander from my side?

LYSANDER

    Lysander's love, that would not let him bide—
    Fair Helena, who more engilds the night
    Than all yon fiery oes and eyes of light.
    Why seek'st thou me? Could not this make thee know,
    The hate I bear thee made me leave thee so?

HERMIA

    You speak not as you think: it cannot be.

HELENA

    Lo, she is one of this confederacy!
    Now I perceive they have conjoin'd all three
    To fashion this false sport, in spite of me.
    Injurious Hermia, most ungrateful maid!
    Have you conspired, have you with these contrived
    To bait me with this foul derision?
    Is all the counsel that we two have shared,
    The sisters' vows, the hours that we have spent
    When we have chid the hasty-footed time
    For parting us—O, is it all forgot?
    All school-days' friendship, childhood innocence?
    And will you rent our ancient love asunder,
    To join with men in scorning your poor friend?
    It is not friendly, 'tis not maidenly:
    Our sex, as well as I, may chide you for it,
    Though I alone do feel the injury.

HERMIA

    I am amazed at your passionate words.
    I scorn you not: it seems that you scorn me.

HELENA

    Have you not set Lysander, as in scorn,
    To follow me and praise my eyes and face?
    And made your other love, Demetrius,
    To call me goddess, nymph, divine and rare,
    Precious, celestial? Wherefore speaks he this
    To her he hates? And wherefore doth Lysander
    Deny your love, so rich within his soul,
    But by your setting on, by your consent?

HERMIA

    I understand not what you mean by this.

HELENA

    Ay, do! Persever, counterfeit sad looks,
    Make mouths upon me when I turn my back;
    Wink each at other; hold the sweet jest up:
    But fare ye well: 'tis partly my own fault;
    Which death or absence soon shall remedy.

LYSANDER

    Stay, gentle Helena; hear my excuse:
    My love, my life, my soul, fair Helena!

HELENA

    O excellent!

HERMIA

    Sweet, do not scorn her so.

DEMETRIUS

    If she cannot entreat, I can compel.

LYSANDER

    Thou canst compel no more than she entreat:
    Helen, I love thee; by my life, I do:

I swear by that which I will lose for thee,
To prove him false that says I love thee not.

DEMETRIUS
  I say I love thee more than he can do.

LYSANDER
  If thou say so, withdraw, and prove it too.

DEMETRIUS
  Quick, come!

HERMIA
  Lysander, whereto tends all this?

LYSANDER
  Away! Away!

DEMETRIUS
  No, no, sir,
  Seem to break loose; take on as you would follow,
  But yet come not. You are a tame man, go!

LYSANDER
  Hang off, thou cat, thou burr! Vile thing, let loose,
  Or I will shake thee from me like a serpent!

HERMIA
  Why are you grown so rude? What change is this?
  Sweet love—

LYSANDER
  Out, loathed medicine! O hated potion, hence!

HERMIA
  Hate me! Wherefore? O me, what news, my love!

Am not I Hermia? Are not you Lysander?
Why, then you left me—O, the gods forbid!—
In earnest, shall I say?

LYSANDER
Ay, by my life;
And never did desire to see thee more.
Therefore be out of hope, of question, of doubt;
Be certain, nothing truer; 'tis no jest
That I do hate thee and love Helena.

HERMIA
O me! You juggler, you canker-blossom,
You thief of love! What, have you come by night
And stolen my love's heart from him?

HELENA
Fine, i'faith!
Have you no modesty, no maiden shame,
No touch of bashfulness? What, will you tear
Impatient answers from my gentle tongue?
Fie, fie, you counterfeit, you puppet, you!

HERMIA
'Puppet'? Why so? Ay, that way goes the game.
Now I perceive that she hath made compare
Between our statures; she hath urged her height;
And with her personage, her tall personage,
Her height, forsooth, she hath prevail'd with him.
And are you grown so high in his esteem
Because I am so dwarfish and so low?
How low am I, thou painted maypole? Speak!
How low am I? I am not yet so low
But that my nails can reach unto thine eyes.

HELENA

    I pray you, though you mock me, gentlemen,
    Let her not hurt me: I was never curst;
    I have no gift at all in shrewishness;
    I am a right maid for my cowardice:
    Let her not strike me. You perhaps may think,
    Because she is something lower than myself,
    That I can match her.

HERMIA

    'Lower'! Hark, again!

HELENA

    Good Hermia, do not be so bitter with me.
    I evermore did love you, Hermia,
    Did ever keep your counsels, never wrong'd you;
    Save that, in love unto Demetrius,
    I told him of your stealth unto this wood.
    And now, so you will let me quiet go,
    To Athens will I bear my folly back
    And follow you no further. Let me go:
    You see how simple and how fond I am.

HERMIA

    Why, get you gone! Who is't that hinders you?

HELENA

    A foolish heart, that I leave here behind.

HERMIA

    What, with Lysander?

HELENA

    With Demetrius.

LYSANDER

    Be not afraid; she shall not harm thee, Helena.

DEMETRIUS

No, sir; she shall not, though you take her part.

HELENA

O, when she's angry, she is keen and shrewd!
She was a vixen when she went to school;
And though she be but little, she is fierce.

HERMIA

'Little' again! Nothing but 'low' and 'little'!
Why will you suffer her to flout me thus?
Let me come to her.

LYSANDER

Get you gone, you dwarf,
You minimus of hindering knot-grass made,
You bead, you acorn.
Now follow, if thou dar'st, to try whose right,
Of thine or mine, is most in Helena.

DEMETRIUS

Follow! Nay, I'll go with thee, cheek by jowl.

(Exeunt LYSANDER and DEMETRIUS.)

HERMIA

You, mistress, all this coil is 'long of you:
Nay, go not back.

HELENA

I will not trust you, I,
Nor longer stay in your curst company.
Your hands than mine are quicker for a fray,
My legs are longer though, to run away.

(Exit.)

HERMIA
    I am amazed, and know not what to say.

(Exit.)

OBERON
    This is thy negligence. Still thou mistak'st,
    Or else committ'st thy knaveries wilfully.

PUCK
    Believe me, king of shadows, I mistook.
    And so far am I glad it so did sort,
    As this their jangling I esteem a sport.

OBERON
    Thou seest these lovers seek a place to fight:
    Hie therefore, Robin, overcast the night,
    And lead these testy rivals so astray
    As one come not within another's way.
    Till o'er their brows death-counterfeiting sleep
    With leaden legs and batty wings doth creep:
    Then crush this herb into Lysander's eye;
    Whose liquor hath a virtuous property.
    When they next wake, all this derision
    Shall seem a dream and fruitless vision.
    Whiles I in this affair do thee employ,
    I'll to my queen and beg her Indian boy;
    And then I will her charmed eye release
    From monster's view, and all things shall be peace.

PUCK
    My fairy lord, this must be done with haste,
    For night's swift dragons cut the clouds full fast.

OBERON
    We may effect this business yet ere day.

(Exit.)

PUCK
Up and down, up and down,
I will lead them up and down:
I am fear'd in field and town:
Goblin, lead them up and down.
Here comes one.

(Re-enter LYSANDER.)

LYSANDER
Where art thou, proud Demetrius? Speak thou now.

PUCK
Here, villain, drawn and ready. Where art thou?

LYSANDER
I will be with thee straight.

PUCK
Follow me then
To plainer ground.

(Exit LYSANDER, as following the voice.)
(Re-enter DEMETRIUS.)

DEMETRIUS
Lysander, speak again!
Thou runaway, thou coward, art thou fled?
Speak! In some bush? Where dost thou hide thy head?

PUCK
Thou coward, art thou bragging to the stars,
Telling the bushes that thou look'st for wars?

DEMETRIUS

    Yea, art thou there?

PUCK

    Follow my voice: we'll try no manhood here.

(Exeunt.)
(Re-enter LYSANDER.)

LYSANDER

    He goes before me and still dares me on:
    When I come where he calls, then he is gone.
    The villain is much lighter-heel'd than I:
    I follow'd fast, but faster he did fly,
    That fallen am I in dark uneven way,
    And here will rest me.

(Lies down.)

    Come, thou gentle day!
    For if but once thou show me thy grey light,
    I'll find Demetrius and revenge this spite.

(Sleeps.)
(Re-enter PUCK and DEMETRIUS.)

PUCK

    Ho, ho, ho! Coward, why com'st thou not?

DEMETRIUS

    Where art thou now?

PUCK

    Come hither: I am here.

DEMETRIUS
   Nay, then, thou mock'st me. Thou shalt buy this dear,
   If ever I thy face by daylight see.
   Now, go thy way. Faintness constraineth me
   To measure out my length on this cold bed.
   By day's approach look to be visited.

(Lies down and sleeps.)
(Re-enter HELENA.)

HELENA
   O weary night, O long and tedious night,
   Abate thy hours! Shine comforts from the east;
   And sleep, that sometimes shuts up sorrow's eye,
   Steal me awhile from mine own company.

(Lies down and sleeps.)

PUCK
   Yet but three? Come one more;
   Two of both kinds make up four.
   Here she comes, curst and sad:
   Cupid is a knavish lad,
   Thus to make poor females mad.

(Re-enter HERMIA.)

HERMIA
   Never so weary, never so in woe,
   I can no further crawl, no further go;
   Here will I rest me till the break of day.
   Heavens shield Lysander, if they mean a fray!

(Lies down and sleeps.)

PUCK

> On the ground
> Sleep sound;
> I'll apply
> To your eye,
> Gentle lover, remedy.

(Squeezing the juice on LYSANDER's eyes.)

> When thou wak'st,
> Thou tak'st
> True delight
> In the sight
> Of thy former lady's eye:
> Jack shall have Jill,
> Naught shall go ill;
> The man shall have his mare again, and all shall be well.

(Exit.)

Act 4, Scene 1

The same. LYSANDER, DEMETRIUS, HELENA, and HER-
MIA lying asleep.

(Enter TITANIA and BOTTOM; PEASEBLOSSOM, COB-
WEB, MUSTARDSEED; OBERON behind unseen.)

TITANIA
    Come, sit thee down upon this flowery bed,
    While I thy amiable cheeks do coy,
    And stick musk-roses in thy sleek smooth head,
    And kiss thy fair large ears, my gentle joy.

BOTTOM
    Where's Peaseblossom?

PEASEBLOSSOM
    Ready.

BOTTOM
    Scratch my head, Peaseblossom. Where's Mounsieur Cobweb?

COBWEB
    Ready.

BOTTOM
    Mounsieur Cobweb, good mounsieur, get you your
    weapons in your hand, and kill me a red-hipped
    humble-bee; and, good mounsieur, bring me the honey-bag.
    And, good mounsieur, have a care the honey-bag break not;
    I would be loath to have you overflown with a
    honey-bag, signior. Where's Mounsieur Mustardseed?

MUSTARDSEED
    Ready.

BOTTOM
>Mounsieur Mustardseed.

MUSTARDSEED
>What's your will?

BOTTOM
>Nothing, good mounsieur, but to help Cavalery Cobweb
>to scratch. I must to the barber's, mounsieur; for
>methinks I am marvellous hairy about the face.

TITANIA
>What, wilt thou hear some music, my sweet love?

BOTTOM
>I have a reasonable good ear in music.

TITANIA
>Or say, sweet love, what thou desir'st to eat.

BOTTOM
>Truly, I could munch your good dry oats. Methinks
>I have a great desire to a bottle of hay. Good hay,
>sweet hay, hath no fellow.

TITANIA
>I have a venturous fairy that shall seek
>The squirrel's hoard, and fetch thee new nuts.

BOTTOM
>I had rather have a handful or two of dried peas.
>But, I pray you, let none of your people stir me; I
>have an exposition of sleep come upon me.

TITANIA
>Sleep thou, and I will wind thee in my arms.
>Fairies, be gone, and be all ways away.

(Exeunt fairies.)

O, how I love thee! How I dote on thee!

(They sleep.)
(Enter PUCK.)

OBERON
    (Advancing.) Welcome, good Robin.
    Seest thou this sweet sight?
    Her dotage now I do begin to pity;
    For, meeting her of late behind the wood,
    Seeking sweet favours from this hateful fool,
    I did upbraid her and fall out with her.
    When I had at my pleasure taunted her
    And she in mild terms begg'd my patience,
    I then did ask of her her changeling child;
    Which straight she gave me, and her fairy sent
    To bear him to my bower in fairy land.
    And now I have the boy, I will undo
    This hateful imperfection of her eyes.
    And, gentle Puck, take this transformed scalp
    From off the head of this Athenian swain,
    That he, awaking when the other do,
    May all to Athens back again repair
    And think no more of this night's accidents
    But as the fierce vexation of a dream.
    But first I will release the fairy queen.
    Be as thou wast wont to be;
    See as thou wast wont to see.
    Dian's bud o'er Cupid's flower
    Hath such force and blessed power.
    Now, my Titania, wake you, my sweet queen.

TITANIA
    My Oberon, what visions have I seen!
    Methought I was enamour'd of an ass.

OBERON
> There lies your love.

TITANIA
> How came these things to pass?
> O, how mine eyes do loathe his visage now!

OBERON
> Sound, music! Come, my queen, take hands with me,
> And rock the ground whereon these sleepers be.

(Music plays.)

> Now thou and I are new in amity,
> And will tomorrow midnight solemnly
> Dance in Duke Theseus' house triumphantly,
> And bless it to all fair prosperity.
> There shall the pairs of faithful lovers be
> Wedded, with Theseus, all in jollity.

PUCK
> Fairy king, attend, and mark:
> I do hear the morning lark.

OBERON
> Then, my queen, in silence sad,
> Trip we after the night's shade;
> We the globe can compass soon,
> Swifter than the wandering moon.

TITANIA
> Come, my lord, and in our flight
> Tell me how it came this night
> That I sleeping here was found
> With these mortals on the ground.

(Exeunt.)

(Horns winded within.)
(Enter THESEUS, HIPPOLYTA, and EGEUS.)

THESEUS
But, soft! What nymphs are these?

EGEUS
My lord, this is my daughter here asleep,
And this, Lysander; this Demetrius is;
This Helena, old Nedar's Helena.

THESEUS
But speak, Egeus, is not this the day
That Hermia should give answer of her choice?

EGEUS
It is, my lord.

THESEUS
Good morrow, friends. Saint Valentine is past:
Begin these wood-birds but to couple now?

*(LYSANDER, DEMETRIUS, HELENA, and HERMIA wake
and start up.)*

LYSANDER
Pardon, my lord.

THESEUS
I pray you all, stand up.
I know you two are rival enemies:
How comes this gentle concord in the world?

LYSANDER
My lord, I shall reply amazedly,
Half sleep, half waking; but as yet, I swear,
I cannot truly say how I came here.

EGEUS

    Enough, enough, my lord; you have enough—
    I beg the law, the law, upon his head!
    They would have stolen away; they would, Demetrius,
    Thereby to have defeated you and me.

DEMETRIUS

    My lord, fair Helen told me of their stealth,
    Of this their purpose hither to this wood;
    And I in fury hither follow'd them,
    Fair Helena in fancy following me.
    But, my good lord, I wot not by what power
    (But by some power it is.), my love to Hermia
    Melted as the snow.
    The object and the pleasure of mine eye
    Is only Helena. To her, my lord,
    Was I betroth'd ere I saw Hermia;
    But, like in sickness, did I loathe this food.
    Now I do wish it, love it, long for it,
    And will for evermore be true to it.

THESEUS

    Fair lovers, you are fortunately met;
    Of this discourse we more will hear anon.
    Egeus, I will overbear your will;
    For in the temple by and by with us
    These couples shall eternally be knit.
    Away with us to Athens. Three and three,
    We'll hold a feast in great solemnity.
    Come, Hippolyta.

(Exeunt THESEUS, HIPPOLYTA, and EGEUS.)

DEMETRIUS

    These things seem small and undistinguishable.

HERMIA
> Methinks I see these things with parted eye,
> When everything seems double.

HELENA
> So methinks;
> And I have found Demetrius like a jewel,
> Mine own, and not mine own.

DEMETRIUS
> Are you sure
> That we are awake? It seems to me
> That yet we sleep, we dream. Do not you think
> The duke was here, and bid us follow him?

HERMIA
> Yea; and my father.

HELENA
> And Hippolyta.

LYSANDER
> And he did bid us follow to the temple.

DEMETRIUS
> Why, then, we are awake. Let's follow him,
> And by the way let us recount our dreams.

(Exeunt.)

BOTTOM
> *(Awaking.)* When my cue comes, call me, and I will
> answer: my next is, 'Most fair Pyramus.' Heigh-ho!
> Peter Quince! Flute, the bellows-mender! Snout,
> the tinker! Starveling! God's my life, stolen

hence, and left me asleep! I have had a most rare vision. I have had a dream, past the wit of man to say what dream it was: man is but an ass, if he go about to expound this dream. Methought I was—there is no man can tell what. Methought I was—and methought I had—I will get Peter Quince to write a ballad of this dream. It shall be called Bottom's Dream, because it hath no bottom; and I will sing it in the latter end of a play, before the duke.

(Exit.)

Act 4, Scene 2

Athens. QUINCE'S house.

(Enter QUINCE, FLUTE, SNOUT, and STARVELING.)

QUINCE
Have you sent to Bottom's house? Is he come home yet?

STARVELING
He cannot be heard of.

FLUTE
If he come not, then the play is marred. It goes
not forward, doth it?

QUINCE
It is not possible. You have not a man in all
Athens able to discharge Pyramus but he.

FLUTE
No, he hath simply the best wit of any handicraft
man in Athens.

QUINCE
Yea, and the best person too; and he is a very
paramour for a sweet voice.

FLUTE
You must say 'paragon.' A paramour is, God bless us,
a thing of naught.

(Enter SNUG.)

SNUG
Masters, the duke is coming from the temple, and

there is two or three lords and ladies more married.
If our sport had gone forward, we had all been made men.

FLUTE
>O sweet bully Bottom!

(Enter BOTTOM.)

BOTTOM
>Where are these lads? Where are these hearts?

QUINCE
>Bottom! O most courageous day! O most happy hour!

BOTTOM
>Masters, I am to discourse wonders—but ask me not
>what; for if I tell you, I am no true Athenian.

QUINCE
>Let us hear, sweet Bottom.

BOTTOM
>Not a word of me. All that I will tell you is, that
>the duke hath dined. Get your apparel together,
>meet presently at the palace; every man look
>o'er his part; for the short and the long is, our
>play is preferred. No more words. Away! Go, away!

(Exeunt.)

Act 5, Scene 1

Athens. The palace of THESEUS.

(Enter THESEUS and HIPPOLYTA.)

HIPPOLYTA
  'Tis strange my Theseus, that these lovers speak of.

THESEUS
  More strange than true. I never may believe
  These antique fables, nor these fairy toys.
  Lovers and madmen have such seething brains,
  Such shaping fantasies, that apprehend
  More than cool reason ever comprehends.

HIPPOLYTA
  But all the story of the night told over,
  And all their minds transfigured so together,
  More witnesseth than fancy's images,
  And grows to something of great constancy;
  But howsoever, strange and admirable.

THESEUS
  Here come the lovers, full of joy and mirth.

(Enter LYSANDER, DEMETRIUS, HERMIA, and HELENA.)

  Joy, gentle friends, joy and fresh days of love
  Accompany your hearts!

LYSANDER
  More than to us
  Wait in your royal walks, your board, your bed!

THESEUS
> Come now; what masques, what dances shall we have
> Between our after-supper and bed-time?
> Is there no play,
> To ease the anguish of a torturing hour?

(Flourish of trumpets.)

> Let him approach.

(Enter QUINCE for the Prologue.)

PROLOGUE
> If we offend, it is with our good will.
> The actors are at hand; and by their show
> You shall know all that you are like to know.

(Enter Pyramus and Thisbe, Wall, Moonshine, and Lion.)

> Gentles, perchance you wonder at this show;
> But wonder on, till truth make all things plain.
> This man is Pyramus, if you would know;
> This beauteous lady Thisby is certain.

(Exeunt Quince, Bottom, Flute, Snug, and Starveling.)

WALL
> In this same interlude it doth befall
> That I, one Snout by name, present a wall;
> And such a wall, as I would have you think,
> That had in it a crannied hole or chink,
> Through which the lovers, Pyramus and Thisby,
> Did whisper often very secretly.
> This loam, this rough-cast and this stone doth show
> That I am that same wall; the truth is so:
> And this the cranny is, right and sinister,
> Through which the fearful lovers are to whisper.

THESEUS
>Would you desire lime and hair to speak better?

DEMETRIUS
>It is the wittiest partition that ever I heard
>discourse, my lord.

(Enter Pyramus.)

THESEUS
>Pyramus draws near the wall: silence!

PYRAMUS
>O grim-look'd night! O night with hue so black!
>O night, which ever art when day is not!
>O night, O night, alack, alack, alack,
>I fear my Thisby's promise is forgot!
>And thou, O wall, O sweet, O lovely wall,
>That stand'st between her father's ground and mine!
>Thou wall, O wall, O sweet and lovely wall,
>Show me thy chink, to blink through with mine eyne!

(Wall holds up his fingers.)

>Thanks, courteous wall; Jove shield thee well for this!
>But what see I? No Thisby do I see.
>O wicked wall, through whom I see no bliss!
>Cursed be thy stones for thus deceiving me!

THESEUS
>The wall, methinks, being sensible, should curse again.

PYRAMUS
>No, in truth, sir, he should not. 'Deceiving me'
>is Thisby's cue: she is to enter now, and I am to
>spy her through the wall.

(Enter Thisbe.)

THISBE
   O wall, full often hast thou heard my moans,
   For parting my fair Pyramus and me!
   My cherry lips have often kiss'd thy stones,
   Thy stones with lime and hair knit up in thee.

PYRAMUS
   I see a voice: now will I to the chink,
   To spy and I can hear my Thisby's face.
   Thisby!

THISBE
   My love! Thou art, my love I think?

PYRAMUS
   Think what thou wilt, I am thy lover's grace.
   O kiss me through the hole of this vile wall!

THISBE
   I kiss the wall's hole, not your lips at all.

PYRAMUS
   Wilt thou at Ninny's tomb meet me straightway?

THISBE
   'Tide life, 'tide death, I come without delay.

(Exeunt Pyramus and Thisbe.)

WALL
   Thus have I, Wall, my part discharged so;
   And, being done, thus Wall away doth go.

(Exit.)

HIPPOLYTA
>This is the silliest stuff that ever I heard.

THESEUS
>The best in this kind are but shadows; and the worst
>are no worse, if imagination amend them.

HIPPOLYTA
>It must be your imagination then, and not theirs.

THESEUS
>If we imagine no worse of them than they of
>themselves, they may pass for excellent men. Here
>come two noble beasts in, a man and a lion.

(Enter Lion and Moonshine.)

LION
>You, ladies, you, whose gentle hearts do fear
>The smallest monstrous mouse that creeps on floor,
>May now perchance both quake and tremble here,
>When lion rough in wildest rage doth roar.
>Then know that I, one Snug the joiner, am
>A lion-fell, nor else no lion's dam.

THESEUS
>A very gentle beast, of a good conscience.
>Let us listen to the moon.

MOONSHINE
>This lanthorn doth the horned moon present—

DEMETRIUS
>He should have worn the horns on his head.

THESEUS

> He is no crescent, and his horns are
> invisible within the circumference.

MOONSHINE

> This lanthorn doth the horned moon present;
> Myself the man i' the moon do seem to be.

THESEUS

> This is the greatest error of all the rest: the man
> should be put into the lanthorn. How is it else the
> man i' the moon?

DEMETRIUS

> He dares not come there for the candle; for, you
> see, it is already in snuff.

HIPPOLYTA

> I am aweary of this moon. Would he would change!

THESEUS

> It appears, by his small light of discretion, that
> he is in the wane; but yet in courtesy, in all
> reason, we must stay the time.

LYSANDER

> Proceed, Moon.

MOONSHINE

> All that I have to say, is, to tell you that the
> lanthorn is the moon and I, the man in the moon.

DEMETRIUS

> But, silence: here comes Thisbe.

(Enter Thisbe.)

THISBE
    This is old Ninny's tomb. Where is my love?

LION
    (Roaring.) Oh—

(Thisbe runs off.)

DEMETRIUS
    Well roared, Lion.

THESEUS
    Well run, Thisbe.

HIPPOLYTA
    Well shone, Moon. Truly, the moon shines with a
    good grace.

(The Lion shakes Thisbe's mantle and exits.)

THESEUS
    Well moused, Lion.

LYSANDER
    And so the lion vanished.

DEMETRIUS
    And then came Pyramus.

(Enter Pyramus.)

PYRAMUS
    Sweet Moon, I thank thee for thy sunny beams;
    I thank thee, Moon, for shining now so bright;
    For, by thy gracious, golden, glittering gleams,
    I trust to take of truest Thisby sight.

But stay—O spite!
But mark, poor knight,
What dreadful dole is here!
Eyes, do you see?
How can it be?
O dainty duck! O dear!
Thy mantle good,
What, stain'd with blood?

THESEUS

This passion, and the death of a dear friend, would
go near to make a man look sad.

HIPPOLYTA

Beshrew my heart, but I pity the man.

PYRAMUS

Out, sword, and wound
The pap of Pyramus;
Ay, that left pap,
Where heart doth hop:

(Stabs himself.)

Thus die I, thus, thus, thus.
Now am I dead,
Now am I fled;
My soul is in the sky.
Tongue, lose thy light;
Moon take thy flight:

(Exit Moonshine.)

Now die, die, die, die, die.

(Dies.)

DEMETRIUS
    No die, but an ace, for him; for he is but one.

LYSANDER
    Less than an ace, man; for he is dead; he is nothing.

THESEUS
    With the help of a surgeon he might yet recover, and prove an ass.

HIPPOLYTA
    How chance Moonshine is gone before Thisbe comes back and finds her lover?

THESEUS
    She will find him by starlight. Here she comes, and her passion ends the play.

(Re-enter Thisbe.)

HIPPOLYTA
    Methinks she should not use a long one for such a Pyramus; I hope she will be brief.

THISBE
    Asleep, my love?
    What, dead, my dove?
    O Pyramus, arise!
    Speak, speak! Quite dumb?
    Dead, dead? A tomb
    Must cover thy sweet eyes.
    These my lips,
    This cherry nose,
    These yellow cowslip cheeks,
    Are gone, are gone!
    Lovers, make moan;

His eyes were green as leeks.
Tongue, not a word!
Come, trusty sword,
Come, blade, my breast imbrue!

(Stabs herself.)

And, farewell, friends;
Thus Thisby ends;
Adieu, adieu, adieu.

(Dies.)

THESEUS
Moonshine and Lion are left to bury the dead.

DEMETRIUS
Ay, and Wall too.

BOTTOM
(Starting up.) No, I assure you, the wall is down that
parted their fathers. Will it please you to see the
epilogue?

THESEUS
No epilogue, I pray you; for your play needs no
excuse. Never excuse; for when the players are all
dead, there needs none to be blamed. Marry, if he
that writ it had played Pyramus and hanged himself
in Thisbe's garter, it would have been a fine
tragedy: and so it is, truly, and very notably
discharged.

(Exeunt.)
(Enter PUCK.)

PUCK

    Now the hungry lion roars,
    And the wolf behowls the moon;
    Whilst the heavy ploughman snores,
    All with weary task fordone.
    And we fairies, that do run
    By the triple Hecate's team
    From the presence of the sun,
    Following darkness like a dream,
    Now are frolic: not a mouse
    Shall disturb this hallow'd house.
    I am sent with broom before,
    To sweep the dust behind the door.

(Enter OBERON and TITANIA, with their train.)

OBERON

    Through the house give gathering light
    By the dead and drowsy fire,
    Every elf and fairy sprite
    Hop as light as bird from brier.

TITANIA

    Hand in hand, with fairy grace,
    Will we sing, and bless this place.

OBERON

    Trip away; make no stay;
    Meet me all by break of day.

(Exeunt OBERON, TITANIA, and train.)

PUCK

    If we shadows have offended,
    Think but this, and all is mended:
    That you have but slumber'd here

While these visions did appear.
And this weak and idle theme,
No more yielding but a dream,
Gentles, do not reprehend;
If you pardon, we will mend.
And, as I am an honest Puck,
If we have unearned luck
Now to 'scape the serpent's tongue
We will make amends ere long;
Else the Puck a liar call.
So, good night unto you all.
Give me your hands, if we be friends,
And Robin shall restore amends.

(Exit.)